THE MARKETS OF YORKSH

by

Elizabeth J. King

HUTTON PRESS

1989

Published by the Hutton Press Ltd.
130 Canada Drive, Cherry Burton, Beverley
East Yorkshire HU17 7SB

Copyright © 1989

Printed and Bound by
Clifford Ward & Co. (Bridlington) Ltd.
55 West Street, Bridlington, East Yorkshire
YO15 3DZ

ISBN 0 907033 80 6

The Publisher acknowledges the cooperation of the following, over the use of photographic material:

The Automobile Association, for sketches from the "AA Roadbook", second post-war edition, 1958.

Calderdale Metropolitan Borough, for illustration from "Under the Clock; the story of the Victorian Borough Market, Halifax", 1983.

The Dalesman Publishing Co. Ltd., for photos from "Life in the Yorkshire Dales", by W.R. Mitchell, 1980.

The Hendon Publishing Co. Ltd., for photos from "Old Yorkshire Recipes", by Joan Poulson, 1974.

Leeds City Council, Department of Municipal Services, for photos of the Leeds Market Hall.

Quickprint (Harrogate) Ltd., for photo from "Visitors Guide to the Harrogate District", 2nd ed. 1977.

Yorkshire Evening Press for material from their photographic library.

Contents

Front cover: Otley Market Place, September 1987.
Reproduced by kind permission of Phillip Rothery.

Acknowledgements

This book owes much to many other people. Firstly, to all those librarians, and other people, throughout the area who have helped me to track down odd pieces of information, answered my queries and have been unfailingly courteous and generous with their time and their knowledge.

Secondly, to all my friends who have shared my love of markets over many years but in particular to those amongst them who have enjoyed with me the delights of such diverse markets as Newark, Kirkbymoorside, Boulogne, St. Raphael and Marrakesh.

Lastly, to those friends in Yorkshire who have accompanied me on some of the 'fieldwork' for this book, pooling their own local knowledge and their enthusiasm for the topic.

My thanks to you all for the happy memories.

Elizabeth J. King,
Horsforth,
April 1989

The Market, Pickering. Reproduced by kind permission of Yorkshire Evening Press.

Introduction

Markets have long been an important part of many towns and villages and in many cases their history goes back hundreds of years. The history and development of the town is often mirrored by the history and development of the market and as a town's fortunes rose or fell, so did the market. This process continues even today with some markets in Yorkshire gradually dwindling away to nearly nothing, like Whitby, whilst others, Malton is a case in point, have been successfully revived.

The early history of markets has much to do with both their geographical position and with the presence, or otherwise, of any castle or religious establishment of power and influence. Local barons built castles in places of strategic importance, like Skipton, the crossroads between East and West, and the religious foundations of Selby and Beverley proved to be very important in the early growth of these places as trading centres. Market and Fair Rights and Charters were eagerly sought after and valuable possessions in their own right. Many of the early ones were in the hands of either the local land-owner or the Church and were normally handed over by the King to those who had his ear! It is interesting to note that some markets are still held on the same day that was stipulated in the Charter. Kirkbymoorside still continues the Wednesday market first started in the early 13th century!

In the early Middle Ages, the local people would come to the Church on Sundays and after the service the market would be held in the church-yard. In 1285, a law was passed forbidding markets to be held in church-yards and this was followed in 1448, by another law forbidding the holding of markets on a Sunday. Existing markets had therefore to move both their place and their day, and the Market Cross, still present in so many places, is to remind traders, once the market was moved from the actual church grounds, 'not to defraud in cheapening'. The earliest form of consumer protection surfaced in the Middle Ages when in 1266 Henry Third passed an act called 'The assize of bread and ale', laying down the standard and weight of what was sold. In many markets there would be an Assize of Bread, an Assize of Ale and usually also an Assize of Measures, this latter often being a standard measure on a church wall or other building against which fabric had to be measured.

Nowadays, the market is still a great draw in many places for both people from the surrounding area and for visitors and tourists. The long tradition of 'going to the market' is still alive and very healthy in many parts of Yorkshire and particularly so in many of the country areas. However, this is not to suggest that some of the larger town markets are not also a great draw for their local community — try Barnsley on a Wednesday to see what I mean! Many of the markets listed in this book have a character and vitality all of their own, reflecting often the particular industries, priorities or concerns of the community. It has been a salutary experience for me to note the very many second-hand clothes stalls (in some cases more resembling a jumble sale) in some parts of Yorkshire and the number of buyers they attract. On the other hand, some markets in the more affluent areas offer expensive, designer knitwear and leather jackets at high prices. Markets in the Humberside area have a wealth of superb fruit and vegetables, so mirroring the very many horticultural small-holdings in that area and if you want to buy cloth, then make a bee-line for places like Huddersfield and Dewsbury.

What is true, though, is that each market is different and there is something new to discover and enjoy in most of them. It may be one of the stalls, it may be the old market place or it may be one of the beautiful Victorian Market Halls still in use in many places. The tragedy, for some places, has been the dead-hand of the planners or 're-development' of shopping areas. For examples of the effect this has had on the markets look at Driffield and Bingley to name but two that have suffered from this awful de-humanising treatment.

I hope that this book will prove useful both to tourists to Yorkshire and to everyone who enjoys pottering around markets. It makes no pretence to be anything but a general interest book, but if any reader does wish to know more about any place mentioned or its history, I would suggest that the local library should be the first call.

Most markets are on for a complete day, setting up around nine o'clock (although this may be later in the winter) and finishing in the late afternoon. However, remember that Sunday markets are usually only allowed to operate in the mornings and some of the smaller markets I found, notably in the South Yorkshire area, also seemed to pack up at lunchtime. In many of the more 'touristy' areas of the county, the summer sees a proliferation of antique and craft fairs, sometimes held in conjunction with the ordinary market. If this is your special interest, the local Tourist Board will probably have details of these events.

Key to use of Book

1. Area Covered. This book takes Yorkshire to be the area so designated before 1974. In other words this is the Yorkshire of the West Riding, the North Riding and the East Riding. Some of these areas now find themselves in Humberside, Cumbria or Cleveland but because they were part of the original Yorkshire, they have been counted as such in this book.

2. Arrangement. Places have been arranged in strict alphabetical order by the name of the town or village. After each place name the present county and district has been added to help with identifying the location of each place.

3. Additional Information. In all cases, the address and phone number of the local library have been included to help visitors who may want extra information about a place before visiting it. Where they exist, the Tourist Information Office has also been listed but some places do not have these and it should also be noted that sometimes they only operate in the summer season anyway. Cattle markets have also been noted when these were known.

I hope you will enjoy these markets as much as I have done. I have tried to visit them all at least once and to ensure that the information is as accurate as possible but any mistakes are all my fault and I apologise in advance for any omissions.

Town. Barnsley.

County. South Yorkshire.

Market Days. Wednesday, Friday, Saturday.
Tuesday: Second-hand.

Where. A modern market hall called the Charter Market Hall and a semi-open stall market leading off this enclosed area. This latter is surrounded by a modern shopping precinct, a multi-storey carpark and even has a pedestrian walkway going overhead. It bears little relation to the old market squares!

Early Closing.   Cattle Market, Monday.
Thursday   Pontefract Road

Central Library,   Tourist Information Office,
Shambles Street,   56, Eldon Street,
Barnsley,   Barnsley,
Tel.0226-733241   Tel.0226-206757

The Archbishop of York gave an early grant to the monks of Pontefract to hold a weekly market on Wednesdays in the Church Field and the market still continues!

The indoor market is very big with a mixture of all sorts of stalls. The food stalls appeared to be very good and to have a wealth of choice. The Wednesday that I visited Barnsley, the whole market area was very busy indeed and packed with local people all with heavy shopping bags. The outside stalls, all more or less permanent fixtures, seemed to have mainly clothes, fabric and household goods. On Tuesdays there is a secondhand market described to me by an elderly Barnsley lady as 'Rag and louse day'!

Town. Batley.

County. Kirklees, West Yorkshire.

Market Days. Friday, Saturday.

Where. An open air market in the Market Place.

Early Closing.
Tuesday.

Public Library,
Market Place,
Batley.
Tel.0924-473141

Batley never had a market charter but public pressure in the 1860's resulted in the establishment of the market in 1868.

The market on Friday is the bigger one and has about 100 stalls with a good variety of things on sale. Fish, grocery, fruit and vegetables and sweets were all well represented and there were about twenty different clothes stalls. A feature of markets in this area is the tripe stall, still doing a good trade. Net curtains, rugs, two comprehensive haberdashery stalls as well as the odd secondhand stall added to the interest here.

Town. Bawtry

County. Doncaster M.B.C. South Yorkshire.

Market Days. Sunday

Where. The Market is at the rear of the Three Counties Enterprise Arcade off the main road through Bawtry.

Early Closing.
Wednesday.

Public Library,
Doncaster Road,
Bawtry.
Tel.0302-710858

To walk into Bawtry on a Sunday morning is quite a novel experience (in this country at least!) Nearly all the shops are open, the car parks are full and there are lots of people wandering about. The market, itself, has a lot of stalls, selling a variety of goods but with food probably least represented, although there is one fruit and vegetable stall on the wide main street away from the rest of the market. However, there are plenty of clothes stalls, household, leather goods, jewellery, D.I.Y., homemade toffee, dried flower arrangements and lots more.

In addition to this market, there is also an Antiques Centre in a near-by street, which is a series of small rooms all packed with interesting curios and furniture.

Town. Bedale.

County. Hambleton D.C. North Yorkshire.

Market Days. Tuesday.

Where. Open air market in the wide main street.

Early Closing.	Cattle Market, Thursday,
Thursday	Bridge Street

Public Library,	Tourist Information Office,
Bedale Hall,	Bedale Hall,
Bedale DL8 1AA.	Bedale DL81AA.
Tel.0677-22053	Tel.0677-24604

In 1251, the first market rights were granted by Henry 3rd, to the then Lord of the Manor, Alan FitzAlan, to hold a market on every Tuesday. This is only a small market with about 30 stalls but it seemed to have a

The Market Cross, Bedale. Reproduced by kind permission of the Automobile Association.

character of its own. The stalls, particularly the fruit and vegetable ones, were all laid out attractively and there was one of the best fish stalls I have seen in any street market. There is an old Market Cross in the Market Place.

Town. Bentham.

County. Craven D.C. North Yorkshire.

Market Days. Wednesday.

Where. The market is held in Cleveland Square, an open area just off the main street. There is also a small covered market held in the Town Hall.

Early Closing.
Thursday

Cattle Market, Wednesday.

Public Library
Central Building,
Bentham.
Tel.0468-61388

Tourist Information Office,
Station Road,
Bentham LA2 7JD.
Tel.0468-62252

The open market is quite small with about twenty stalls selling the usual range of goods. I visited it in the winter and it may be that there are more stalls in the summer time. The Market Hall had some second-hand books and china as well as a plant stall and a clothes stall.

Town. Beverley.

County. Beverley District, Humberside.

Market Days. Saturday.

Where. There are two market squares in Beverley. The Wednesday Market Square is slightly smaller than the Saturday Market Square and these are divided by Toll Gavel, originally the place in the Middle Ages where people paid their taxes, although now it is a modern shopping street.

Early Closing.
Thursday

Cattle Market, Monday,
Tuesday, Wednesday.

Public Library
Champney Road,
Beverley HU17 9BQ.
Tel.0482-867108

Tourist Information Office,
The Guildhall,
Register Square,
Beverley
Tel.0482-882255

The early growth of this market was due to the large Priory and its Charter granted by Archbishop Thurston of York in 1129.

In the Saturday market there is a very large Market cross, erected in 1714, and supported by eight columns each one of an entire piece of stone. There are four crests on the cross, one of Queen Anne, one Beverley Borough, and one each for the Hotham and Warton families who paid for the building of the cross. In one corner of the Saturday market, there is quite a pleasant Corn Exchange built in 1886.

This is a market well worth a visit! It's a big market with a large choice from lots of fruit and vegetable stalls, clothes, household goods etc. to cutlery, hats, sheepskins and pictures! There were also many fabrics and wool stalls - the Saturday I was there I counted at least eight specialising in these. It is a most pleasant market to potter around and enjoy the variety.

A W.I. Market is held each Friday morning in the Memorial Hall, Lairgate.

Beverley Market Place in 1830. Reproduced by kind permission of Hendon Publishing Co. Ltd.

Town. Bingley.

County. Bradford M.B.C. West Yorkshire.

Market Days. Wednesday, Friday.

Where. Covered extension to a shopping precinct up Chapel Lane.

Early Closing.
Tuesday

Public Library
Myrtle Walk,
Bingley.
Tel.0274-568697

Bingley used to have a Market Place and a Butter Cross but these were removed by the Bingley Development Corporation, pre-1891! The old Market Cross is now re-sited near to the Bingley Arts Centre and very close to the original site. What is now called the 'market' is really a travesty of the term. In reality it is a very few stalls tacked on at the end of a modern shopping precinct.

Town. Birstall.

County. Kirklees M.B.C. West Yorkshire.

Market Days. Thursday.

Where. Open market in a cobbled Market Place in the centre of this small town.

Early Closing.
Tuesday

Public Library,
Market Place,
Birstall.
Tel.0924-472793

After a lapse of many years, the market was revived in the late 1930's. Although not directly connected with the market, there is a statue in the market square of Joseph Priestley, the discoverer of oxygen, who was born at Fieldhead, Birstall in 1733.

This is a small market of about thirty stalls with the usual selection of goods. Clothes, fruit and vegetables, a fish van and a grocery stall, cards, pet foods and household goods are all to be found here.

Town. Boroughbridge.

County. Harrogate D.C. North Yorkshire.

Market Days. Monday.

Where. Open market in the Back Lane car park.

Early Closing.   Cattle Market, Monday.
Thursday

Public Library,   Tourist Information Office,
St. James Square,   Fishergate,
Boroughbridge.   Boroughbridge.
Tel.0423-322649   Tel.0423-323373

Piers Gaveston, the then Lord of the Manor, granted a Charter in the 14th century to hold a weekly market in the town and there is also Barnaby Fair, held each year in June, which was created by the Charter of Charles

2nd. in 1682, and attracts dealers from all over the north to buy and sell horses and ponies. The Market Cross is a relatively new one having been built in 1875.

The weekly market is small with only about 15 stalls. A Fish van seems to do a good trade and a local nurseryman sells both produce and plants.

Town. Bradford.

County. West Yorkshire.

Market Days. Monday to Saturday.

Where. There are three covered markets in Bradford. Rawson market, an old Victorian building, Kirkgate market which is part of a modern shopping mall and John Street market built to replace the old open market.

Early Closing.
Wednesday

Central Library, Princes Way, Bradford BD1 1NN Tel.0274-753600	Tourist Information Office, City Hall, Hall Ings, Channing Way, Bradford BD1 1HY. Tel.0274-753678

The very first Charter was granted by Henry 3rd. in the 12th century, although the markets have altered drastically since then! Look at the Rawson market, an old Victorian building, although it does not have quite the grandeur of some of the other Yorkshire Victorian market halls.

The Rawson market is in some ways the most interesting and has the most character. It houses all the butchers, fishmongers and most of the fruit and vegetable stalls as well as some other food shops. The Kirkgate market and the John Street complex both have very many units, but are more like small shops, particularly in the case of the Kirkgate market.

Town. Bridlington.

County. East Yorkshire D.C. Humberside.

Market Days. Wednesday, Saturday.

Where. This is quite a large open street market on both sides of King Street.

Early Closing.
Thursday

Public Library, King Street, Bridlington. Tel.0262-672917	Tourist Information Office, 25 Princes Street, Bridlington YO15 2NP Tel.0262-673474

There has been a market here since King John granted a Charter in 1200, although over the centuries the market appears to have moved from one area to another in the town. However by about 1890, the market seems to have settled in King Street and there it still remains. This is an attractive market with stalls on both sides of this wide street. Lots of really good fruit and vegetables — a reflection perhaps of the very many small-holdings and horticultural enterprises in this area. Also plenty of other things to buy from cleaner spares to pictures! I enjoyed pottering along the varied stalls.

Town. Brighouse.

County. Calderdale M.B.C. West Yorkshire.

Market Days. Wednesday, Saturday.

Where. The market is a semi-open one by the canal.

Early Closing.
Tuesday

Public Library,
Rydings Park,
Halifax Road,
Brighouse HD6 2AF
Tel.0484-718639

There are about sixty stalls in a semi-open space at the side of the canal. Lots of variety but with many clothes and shoes. The Wednesday I visited it, there were some secondhand stalls, fabrics and wool, grocery, as well as about five fruit and vegetable, one fish and some meat and delicatessen. The market is in a pleasant setting with the canal running alongside it.

Town. Castleford.

County. Wakefield M.D.C. West Yorkshire.

Market Days. Monday, Friday, Saturday.
(Thursday — Second-hand and craft).

Where. The open stalls are in Carlton Street and there is a covered Market Hall also in Carlton Street.

Early Closing.
Wednesday

Public Library,
Carlton Street,
Castleford.
Tel.0977-559552

The market here seems to have been established in the 1860's and the Market Hall was built in 1879. Unfortunately the interior was burnt out in 1929 but the fine facade still survives although additions were made in 1963.

This is a busy, bustling urban market with a great

variety of stalls in the open air part with a wealth of choice, particularly in clothes and shoes. On Saturdays there are about 100 stalls of which about 50 are clothing. There were only 9 stalls selling food but lots of toys and bric-a-brac as well as some secondhand clothing stalls and some with secondhand china and glass, books, records, tapes and even videos. Vacuum cleaner spares and bags, sports equipment, working overalls and baby equipment were all in evidence outside. The indoor market is very large with a wealth of stalls and choice. There are lots of food stalls of all sorts as well as everything else you could want to buy. Castleford is an interesting, satisfying market with a quite distinct character of its own, reflecting very much the community in which it operates.

Town. Cleckheaton.

County. Kirklees. West Yorkshire.

Market Days. Outdoor Market-Tuesday, Saturday.
Indoor Market Hall - Monday to Saturday.

Where. A modern indoor market hall with a small open space at the side for the open stall market.

Early Closing.
Wednesday

Public Library,
Whitcliffe Road,
Cleckheaton.
Tel.0274-873856

The market here is not very old having only started in the latter part of the 19th century. The indoor market is now housed in a small, bright, modern building with a good range of mainly food shops, although other things are also available. The outdoor market is not very big, but has quite a good choice.

Town. Denaby Main.

County. Doncaster M.B.C. South Yorkshire.

Market Days. Tuesday-bric-a-brac.
Friday-General retail.

Where. Open air in Market Place.

Early Closing.
Wednesday.

Public Library,
Church Street,
Denaby Main.
Tel.0709-862316

I visited here on a Tuesday when it was the bric-a-brac and secondhand stalls. It is only a small market and when I was there not every stall was occupied. Many of the stalls had secondhand clothing although some also had china, books and secondhand household goods. One or two stalls offered new toys, cards and stationery etc. but most of the items were for re-sale. There were about fifty stalls in total.

Town. Dewsbury.

County. Kirklees. West Yorkshire.

Market Days. The Open Market is on Wednesday and Saturday, with a secondhand market on a Friday, but the Indoor Market Hall is open every day although many units only open on Wednesday, Friday and Saturday.

Where. The splendid Market Hall is in Corporation Street and the open market is Cloth Hall Street next to it.

Early Closing.
Tuesday.

Public Library,
Wellington Road,
Dewsbury.
Tel.0924-465151

The Market Hall is a lovely old Victorian building with lots of wrought iron work and red and blue paint, now looking in need of some refurbishment but still well worth a visit to see it.

The open market has some rather ugly corrugated iron roofed stalls but the whole area is alive with bustle and business. A modern unit houses seven butchers shops. The market seems to have had a long history in Dewsbury, probably starting in the Middle Ages, but lapsed and was then re-established in 1740 by the Duke of Newcastle.

This is a very big market with about forty stalls inside and around 360 outside. Lots of everything but especially good for clothes, fabrics and wool. There are also some stalls selling carpets. Look out for the two tripe stalls both doing a brisk trade and offering a 'take-away' service. Neatsfoot oil, a by-product, is sold on Gothards Tripe stall and is popular to cure bruises, rheumatism etc. It will also soften leather! Put Dewsbury on your visiting list!

Town. Dinnington.

County. Rotherham M.B.C. South Yorkshire.

Market Days. Friday and Saturday for the open market but Tuesday, Thursday, Friday and Saturday for the Market Hall.

Where. The open market is behind a modern shopping centre on the main road through Dinnington and the Market Hall is a little further up the same road.

Early Closing.
Wednesday.

Public Library,
Laughton Road,
Dinnington.
Tel.0909-562329

The market is quite large for such a relatively small place and was full of shoppers on the Friday I was there. Fish, fruit and vegetables, sweets and cakes were all here but again with many clothes stalls. Some secondhand and curio stalls were also here.

The Market Hall had a good choice of mainly household goods and clothing, but outside it were some stalls selling fish, flowers and fruit!

Town. Doncaster.

County. South Yorkshire.

Market Days. Tuesday, Friday, Saturday.
Wednesday — antiques and curios.

Where. This is such a large market that you cannot really miss it! It spreads over a wide area of the town, principally in the Market Square but there is also a covered market in the old Corn Exchange.

Early Closing.   Cattle Market, Tuesday.
Tuesday.   Chapel Drive.

Central Library,   Tourist Information Office,
Waterdale,   Central Library,
Doncaster DN1 3JE   Waterdale,
Tel.0302-734305   Doncaster DN1 3JE
                            Tel.0302-734909

Doncaster has a very long market history and its first Charter was granted by King John in the 13th century, with the original market conveniently sited both near to the Wharf but also an extension of the church-yard of St. Mary Magdalene (now the site of the Corn Exchange). This latter building was erected in 1873 and also housed a concert hall. Inside it are rather tatty stalls but it is still worth a good look and is a good example of Victorian wrought iron and glass work.

Altogether this is a superb and very large market with about 300 open stalls as well as a huge number of units in the covered areas. It would be difficult to think of anything you could not buy here! I visited the market on a Tuesday but am told that it is even bigger on a Friday or Saturday. Well worth a visit.

Town. Driffield.

County. East Yorkshire D.C. Humberside.

Market Days. Thursday, Saturday.

Where. The market is housed in a modern and very 'characterless' market hall leading off the main street.

Early Closing.   Cattle Market, Thursday.
Wednesday

Public Library,
Cross Hill,
Driffield.
Tel.0377-43393

I understand that this has replaced an open market which used to operate here and that at the time of change, there was considerable local opposition. Having seen it for myself, I can well understand the feeling against it. It bears little relationship at all to a market and is a travesty of 'planning'. There were a number of different small units in the hall selling a reasonable variety, but, although it was a Saturday morning when I was there, it was very quiet.

Town. Easingwold.

County. Hambleton D.C. North Yorkshire.

Market Days. Friday.

Where. Market Place.

Early Closing.
Wednesday

Public Library,   Tourist Information Office,
Market Place,   Chapel Lane,
Easingwold.   Easingwold.
Tel.0347-21706   Tel.0347-21530

It was not until 1639 that George Hall obtained Letters Patent for himself and his heirs from Charles 1st. to hold a Friday market (although Fair Rights had existed here since 1291), and he chose the central square in Easingwold for this.

The Butter Cross is a rebuilding of an old cross and the circle of cobbles in the Market Place, between the Butter Market and the north end of the Town Hall, marks the site of an old bear-baiting ring. This new Town Hall, at the rear of the market, was opened in March 1864 to replace an earlier one damaged by fire.

This is a small market with only about 10 stalls, selling fruit and vegetables, some home-made cakes and a nice cheese and bacon stall. Plants from local nurseries were also to be found.

Town. Edlington.

County. Doncaster M.B.C. South Yorkshire.

Market Days. Thursday.

Where. The Market is on a fairly large open site on the main road through the town.

Public Library,
The Crescent,
Edlington.
Tel.0709-863259

The market has about 30 stalls but as is often the case with these smaller markets, roughly half the stalls are selling clothes. However, there were some secondhand and bric-a-brac stalls, household goods and a whole-food stall as well as a variety of other goods and food on offer.

Town. Elland.

County. Calderdale M.D.C. West Yorkshire.

Market Days. Friday.

Where. The Market is held in Timber Street.

Early Closing.
Tuesday.

Public Library,
Coronation Street,
Elland HX5 0DF.
Tel.0422-74472

In 1317, Edward First granted a Charter to John de Eland to hold both a market and two fairs, but as Halifax gained in importance so the market here dwindled and although it is a pleasant market, it is not very large. It offers the usual selection of clothes stalls, household goods, a few food stalls and a large haberdashery/wool stall. Toys, pet foods, books and bric-a-brac were also to be found.

Town. Featherstone.

County. Wakefield M.B.C. West Yorkshire.

Market Days. Thursday.

Where. An open area in a modern shopping precinct in Station Lane.

Early Closing.
Wednesday.

Public Library,
Victoria Street,
Featherstone.
Tel.0977-780413

This is quite a small market but with a reasonable variety of both food and other goods. The Thursday I visited there were quite a few people around although it was still early. It did not have quite the emphasis on clothes that many of the smaller markets seem to suffer from.

Town. Garforth.

County. Leeds M.D.C. West Yorkshire.

Market Days. Saturday.

Where. Open market off Main Street.

Early Closing.
Wednesday.

Public Library,
Lidgett Lane,
Garforth.
Tel.0532-865271

This is a small, open stall market with about 20 stalls. Fruit and vegetable, fish and a sweet stall are there, as are six clothing stalls. An unusual stall was one selling reproduction furniture!

Town. Goldthorpe.

County. Barnsley M.B.C. South Yorkshire.

Market Days. Tuesday, Saturday.

Where. The open stalls are there permanently in Market Street.

Early Closing.
Wednesday.

Public Library,
Queen Street,
Goldthorpe.
Tel.0709-893278

A small market serving this predominately mining community. There are about thirty stalls with the usual mixture of foods, clothes and household goods. There were also some secondhand clothes stalls and a few shop units with meat, bakery etc.

Town. Goole.

County. Boothferry D.C. Humberside.

Market Days. Wednesday, Friday, Saturday.

Where. A brick built Market Hall in Boothferry Road.

Early Closing.
Wednesday.

Cattle Market, Monday.
Aire Street.

Public Library,
Carlisle Street,
Goole.
Tel.0405-2187

Tourist Information Office,
Public Library,
Carlisle Street.
Tel.0405-2187

Public Library,
90 Westgate,
Guisborough TS14 6AP.
Tel.0287-32668

Tourist Information Office,
Fountain Street,
Guisborough TS14 6QF.
Tel.0287-33801

Goole is a relatively modern town and so the Market only really started in the latter part of the last century. The Market Hall was built in 1896 and there is a modern extension leading from it. There are a few permanent outside stalls which are really more like small shop units. This is really just a market hall with a few 'outside' stalls which hardly constitute a street market.

Great Driffield *see* **Driffield**

Town. Guisborough.

County. Langbaugh D.C. Cleveland.

Market Days. Thursday, Saturday.

Where. Market Place.

Early Closing.
Wednesday.

The Prior of Guisborough was granted a right to hold a market in 1263, but it is probable that one existed before then on open land in front of the Priory. This right was transferred in 1558 by Queen Mary to Sir Thomas Challoner and, unusually, this right is still in private ownership — that of Lord Guisborough! The market moved to Marske for a short period in 1667 because of the presence of plague in Guisborough, but moved back as soon as the danger was passed. The Market Cross now seems to act as a mini-roundabout and seems to date from the early 19th century although it almost certainly replaced a much earlier one. The Town Hall is built on the site of a former Tolbooth and Shambles.

This is a really splendid market full of interest and variety. It was very busy on the Thursday I was there with about 70 stalls. Lots of good food, (including a cheese van with bow window and a huge choice), clothes, household, brassware, records, cleaner spares — you name it and it's here! Look at all the lovely striped awnings on the stalls — other street markets could learn a thing or two! Definitely on the list of markets not to be missed.

There is a W.I. Market on Thursday p.m. in Sunnyfield House, Westgate.

Town. Halifax.

County. Calderdale, West Yorkshire.

Market Days. Borough Market (Covered market hall) Monday to Saturday.
Piece Hall. Friday, Saturday.
Piece Hall. Thursday-Flea and Second-hand.

Where. The Covered Borough Market is in the centre of the town, with various entrances, and The Piece Hall is just around the corner.

Early Closing.
Thursday.

Central Library,
Northgate,
Halifax.
Tel.0422-57257

Tourist Information Office,
The Piece Hall,
Halifax HX1 1RE.
Tel.0422-68725

The Borough Market is a relatively new institution dating originally from 1810 when an Act of Parliament gave Market Rights to a private company, but the Piece Hall was originally built for the sale of wool cloth and then rebuilt in 1770. This is a most splendid four-sided

HALIFAX,
MAY 2d, 1810.

WHEREAS

It hath been repeatedly reprefented that the

SHOPS

in the

New-Market,

Are OPENED on SUNDAYS

For the Sale of Provifions, to the great Difcredit of the Police of the Town, and in flagrant Oppofition to the Laws of the Country:

The Conftables of Halifax

HEREBY GIVE NOTICE,

That it is their Determination to ufe all Authority within their Power, to put a Stop to fuch Practice; and do caution all Butchers, Huckfters, and others throughout the Town, againft opening their Shops, expofing to fale, or felling on the Lord's Day, as they are refolved to do their Duty in profecuting all fuch Offenders.

JOHN WATERHOUSE,
CHRISTOPHER RAWSON, } Constables.

Jacobs, Printer, Engraver, &c. Halifax.

Advertisement for the Borough Market, Halifax. Reproduced by kind permission of Calderdale Amenities & Recreation Department.

building with a central, large open area and has been restored and refurbished to make a most attractive, interesting and unique building. It must be one of the most imaginative redevelopments, and the shops that are housed in the colonnades around the square and the stalls in the middle all make for an experience not to be missed. The Borough Market, too, has much to see and interest the stranger. There is the most fascinating ornate clock housed in this lovely light airy building with its glass roof, and, although it more resembles small 'shop units' rather than a market, it is still full of atmosphere and character. Note also the beautiful decorated iron gates at both this market and the Piece Hall. Halifax has so much to offer the enthusiastic 'marketeer' that it should rate a gold star!

Town. Harrogate.

County. Harrogate D.C. North Yorkshire.

Market Days. Monday to Saturday.

Where. Covered Market Hall opening off the old Market Place in the now modernised and pedestrianised shopping area.

Early Closing.
Wednesday.

Public Library,
Victoria Avenue,
Harrogate HG1 1EG,
Tel.0423-502774

Tourist Information Office,
Royal Baths Assembly Rooms,
Crescent Road,
Harrogate.
Tel.0423-525666

This is very much on the borderline of a 'market' as it is all individual shop-type units, permanent and open most days. A lower floor sells mostly house-hold, bric-a-brac and D.I.Y. whilst all the food shops are on the ground floor. There are approximately 50 units in all.

Town. Hawes.

County. Richmond, North Yorkshire.

Market Days. Tuesday.

Where. The market stretches down one side of the main street, but the Market Hall and one or two stalls are on the opposite side of the road.

Early Closing.
Wednesday.

Public Library,
Market Hall,
Hawes,
Tel.096-97-613

Tourist Information Office,
National Park Centre,
Station Road,
Hawes DL8 3NT.
Tel.096-97-450

Hawes Market. Reproduced by kind permission of Dalesman Publishing Ltd.

Hawes claims to be the highest market town in Yorkshire, but it did not obtain its Market Charter until 1705 when a teacher from Gayle bought it from William 3rd. for £600!

This is not a very large market, but it is an interesting one with some unusual stalls. Herb jellies, together with locally made home-made sweets and cakes were on sale at one stall, leather tankards at another and there was even a travelling travel agent! The Market Hall housed some other traders — a wholefood stall, shoes, haberdashery etc.

Town. Hebden Bridge.

County. Calderdale M.B.C. West Yorkshire.

Market Days. Thursday.

Where. The market is in Valley Road and there is also a very small flea market in a building on the opposite side of the road.

Early Closing.
Tuesday.

Public Library,
Cheetham Street,
Hebden Bridge,
Tel.0422-842151

Tourist Information Office,
1 Bridge Gate,
Hebden Bridge HX7 8SP.
Tel.0422-843831

Here is a bustling market serving this Pennine community. Clothes stalls are most in evidence but there is also a good stall selling cheese (including some Yorkshire varieties) and bacon, one with nothing else but tapes and cassettes and a selection of good quality towels and linen. A nice market with about 30 stalls in a very interesting old town.

Town. Heckmondwike.

County. Kirklees M.B.C. West Yorkshire.

Market Days. Tuesday, Saturday.

Where. The market spreads itself all over this small town and can hardly be missed!

Early Closing.
Wednesday.

Public Library,
Walkley Lane,
Heckmondwike.
Tel.0924-403764

The first record of a market here appears to be in 1760, although it seems that nearby Dewsbury fought tooth and nail to try to keep away any potential competition!

There is a nice ornate clock and fountain by the market which was put up to commemorate the marriage of the then Prince of Wales and Princess Alexandra of Denmark in 1863. It is decorated in black and gold and surrounded by black railings topped with gold points.

The market is much bigger than you initially think with stalls spread over two or three streets. Some interesting stalls included one selling lovely Indian cloths for saris and what appeared to be a very 'up-market' stall selling famous makes of perfume! Another stall that attracted a large queue was one selling ham and potted meat — obviously very popular with the locals. Embroidery as well as haberdashery stalls were here, lots of clothes, fabrics, three fish stalls — one with game as well, good fruit and vegetables. Altogether an interesting market.

Town. Hedon.

County. Humberside.

Market Days. Wednesday.

Where. Market Place.

Early Closing.
Thursday.

Public Library,
31 St. Augustine Gate,
Hedon HU12 8EU.
Tel.0482-897651

The Market Place, Helmsley. Reproduced by kind permission of Yorkshire Evening Press.

The market has only recently been resurrected here and is still only fairly small with about twenty or so stalls. Clothes, fruit and vegetables and general household goods are all here and although Hedon is now part of Hull, it still has some fine old buildings with the Town Hall, built in 1683, in the Market Place. There is also a very old cross, said to commemorate the landing of Henry 4th. in 1399 but this is now erected in the grounds of an old people's home, Holyrood House.

Town. Helmsley.

County. Ryedale D.C. North Yorkshire.

Market Days. Friday.

Where. Open market in the Market Place.

Early Closing.
Wednesday.

Public Library,
The Court House,
Helmsley.
Tel.0439-70619

Tourist Information Office,
Town Hall,
Helmsley YO6 5DL.
Tel.0439-70173

The earliest reference to a market here seems to date from 1285, but the market has definitely existed on this same site since 1467. Originally it was held in the Church yard and the Market Cross stood there before being moved to its present site in the Market Place. The Cross appears to be of relatively recent origin but the shaft is that of the ancient cross. The spired monument in the Market Place is to Lord Feversham who died in 1867 and the memorial to him was erected two years after his death at a cost of £800! The Town Hall was built in 1901 in the style of an old Tolbooth to replace an earlier covered market and Tolbooth which had stood there since at least 1637.

I came here on a Friday in January and the market was relatively quiet. However, having known this market well over many years, this was very unusual and it is certainly worth a visit. Lots of interesting stalls — an organic fruit and vegetable stall, nice cheese and bacon, books and bric-a-brac, pictures, working clothes and a fish van from Scarborough that always has a long queue!

Town. Hemsworth.

County. Wakefield M.B.C. West Yorkshire.

Market Days. Monday, Friday, Saturday.

Where. Quite a large open area off Kirkby Road and bounded on one side by Market Street.

Early Closing.
Wednesday.

Public Library,
Market Street,
Hemsworth.
Tel.0977-610170

Clothes, as often seems to be the case in the smaller markets, seemed to predominate on the Saturday that I visited, but there were also a surprising number of grocery and confectionery stalls amongst the sixty or so stalls. There was one stall selling bags of various cake and bread mixes, even including a Yorkshire Pudding mix!

Town. Holmfirth.

County. Kirklees M.B.C. West Yorkshire.

Market Days. Thursday. (A Craft Market is also held on Saturdays between Easter and Christmas).

Where. The open market with its semi-permanent stalls is held in Crown Bottom.

Early Closing.
Tuesday.

Cattle Market, Tuesday, Riverside.

Public Library,
Huddersfield Road,
Holmfirth.
Tel.0484-682231

Tourist Information Office,
49/51, Huddersfield Road,
Holmfirth HD7 1JP.
Tel.0484-684992

It would seem that the market was first established in 1909, and this followed on from the success of the Holmfirth Cattle Market which had started in 1901.

It's a varied, small market with about thirty stalls selling everything from carpets and rugs to pet food. As with many markets, clothes stalls seem to predominate but there is also a good selection of fruit and vegetables, a fish stall and sweets and confectionery.

Town. Hornsea.

County. Holderness D.C. Humberside.

Market Days. Sunday.

Where. Sands Lane, Hornsea.

Early Closing.
Wednesday.

Public Library,
77 Newbiggin,
Hornsea,
Tel.0964-532561

Tourist Information Office,
Floral Hall,
Esplanade,
Hornsea HU18 1NQ.
Tel.0964-2919

There are approximately eighty stalls here selling mainly clothes, but also household goods. Food stalls are very much in a minority! Unlike some other Sunday markets, it is open in the afternoon as well as the morning.

Town. Hoyland.

County. Barnsley, M.B.C. South Yorkshire.

Market Days. Tuesday, Saturday.

Where. The Market is in quite a pleasant large open area in the centre.

Early Closing.
Wednesday.

Public Library,
Sheffield Road,
Hoyland.
Tel.0226-744279

There are about fifty stalls here with the usual variety

of food, clothes and household goods, but the market does not seem to have any special character of its own.

Town. Huddersfield.

County. Kirklees, West Yorkshire.

Market Days. The Open Market, Monday, Thursday, Saturday.
Secondhand Market, Tuesday, Saturday.
Market Hall, Monday to Saturday.

Where. The Open Market is in Brook Street, and the Indoor Market Hall in Queensgate.

Early Closing. Cattle Market, Monday.
Wednesday

Central Library,
Princess Alexandra Walk,
Huddersfield HD1 2SU.
Tel.0484-513808

Tourist Information
Office,
3/5 Albion Street,
Huddersfield HD1 2NW.
Tel.0484-22133

The Market Hall is a fine Victorian building of elegant appearance with much glass and ornate ironwork. Carved shields at the entrances to the market bear the arms of Charles 2nd. who gave the original market charter to John Ramsden in 1672. The building was restored in 1980 and won a Civic Trust Commendation in 1983. It celebrated its 100th anniversary on 1.8.1988. There is an old Market Cross, erected in 1683, in the Market Place.

If you are interested in buying fabrics then this must be the market for you. Although most markets have one or two stalls for material, Huddersfield topped the league table with at least ten selling a variety of fabrics, curtaining etc. Carpet and rug stalls were also more numerous so reflecting some of the local industries. The Market Hall had most of the food stalls, including a West Indian food and vegetable stall, as well as clothing, D.I.Y. Household etc. Outside there were about 70 stalls, lots of clothing but also many haberdashery and sewing materials. Most unusually, but doing a very good trade, was an organic fruit and vegetable stall with a variety of produce. An interesting market, not least because of the lovely building, but also one reflecting very much the local area.

Town. Hull.

County. Humberside.

Market Days. The outside market is on Tuesday, Friday and Saturday, but the Kings Market Hall is open all week.

Where. The Kings Market Hall opens off Trinity House Lane and the outside market is in the square just behind

29

this. The stalls nestle around the sides and in front of Holy Trinity Church.

Early Closing.
Thursday

Cattle Market, Monday.

Public Library, Albion Street, Hull HU1 3TF. Tel.0482-224040	Tourist Information Office, 75/76 Carr Lane, Hull HU1 3RD. Tel.0482-223559

The Market Hall was built in 1902 and is a pleasing building with arches and windows with balconies. When I visited it, repair work appeared to be going on to the exterior of the building. The outside market is in the large area by the Church and in the same square is a small museum, previously the old Grammar School, where both Andrew Marvell and William Wilberforce went to school. The indoor market appeared to have most of the food and the outside market was a little disappointing for such a relatively large city. There were lots of clothes stalls (including one advertising 'teaser lingerie'!), secondhand jewellery, hats, lace curtains and watches. There were not many people around although it was a lovely day and the town itself was busy.

There are three other markets in suburbs of Hull. Bransholme has a Market Hall in a modern shopping development, Cottingham has a market on Tuesday, and Orchard Park on a Thursday.

Town. Ingleton.

County. Craven D.C. North Yorkshire.

Market Days. Friday.

Where. In the Square.

Early Closing.
Thursday.

Public Library, Main Street, Ingleton. Tel.052-42-41758	Tourist Information Office, Community Centre Car Park Main Street, Ingleton. Tel.052-42-41049

This is only a very small market with about nine or ten stalls and although the visit was in winter-time I do not think the market is much bigger in the summer. Greengrocers, a butchers, pet-foods and sweets were represented but the other stalls were clothes, wool and household goods, with nothing particularly striking.

Town. Keighley.

County. Bradford M.B.C. West Yorkshire.

Market Days. Monday to Saturday.

Where. Covered Market Hall built near to a modern shopping precinct and opened in 1971.

Early Closing.
Tuesday.

Public Library,
North Street,
Keighley.
Tel.0274-758210

The first market Charter was granted in 1305 by Edward 1st to Henry de Keighley, but the so-called 'market' is now a rather 'sanitised' and characterless collection of about eighty permanent shop units selling a wide range of goods. Two large haberdashery stalls reflect the sewing skills of much of this area.

Town. Killamarsh.

County. Sheffield M.B.C. South Yorkshire.

Market Days. Thursday.

Where. A square in the centre of Killamarsh in a modern shopping developoment called Parkside.

Early Closing.
Wednesday.

There is no Public Library in Killamarsh

A small, though quite busy market, in this small town. Mostly clothes stalls but also quite a lot of food as well as one stall selling carpets and rugs and two toy stalls.

Kingston-upon-Hull *see* **Hull.**

Town. Kirkbymoorside.

County. Ryedale D.C. North Yorkshire.

Market Days. Wednesday.

Where. Open street market down both sides of the wide, cobbled main street. There are also some stalls in the Memorial Hall.

Early Closing.
Thursday.

Public Library,
Literary Institute,
Church Street,
Kirkbymoorside.
Tel.0751-31098

Records exist back to the early 13th century of a Wednesday market in Kirkbymoorside, so there is a

The Shambles, rear of the Market Place, Kirbymoorside. Reproduced by kind permission of Yorkshire Evening Press.

continuous history of a Wednesday market here for over seven hundred years.

The Tolbooth, now known as the Memorial Hall, was originally built in the early 18th century although, after a fire destroyed it, it was rebuilt in 1871. Here, farmers' wives paid a penny toll to sell their wares. Behind this Hall is a very old Market Cross and a narrow street still called The Shambles with some now unused old shops.

This is a real country market, drawing people from all the surrounding country-side. A good variety of stalls with lots of fruit and vegetables, fish, a good cheese stall, clothes, whole-foods, some bric-a-brac, plants, etc. The day I visited, the Hall had some antique stalls as well as some hand-made woollies and secondhand goods. Put this market on your list for its character and atmosphere.

Town. Knaresborough.

County. Harrogate D.C. North Yorkshire.

Market Days. Wednesday.

Where. The Market Place — a large open area in the centre of the town.

Early Closing. Thursday.   Cattle Market, Monday.

The old chemist's shop, Knaresborough. Reproduced by kind permission of Quickprint of Harrogate.

Knaresborough Market Place in 1904. Reproduced by kind permission of Hendon Publishing Co. Ltd.

Public Library,
Market Place,
Knaresborough.
Tel.0423-863054

Tourist Information Office,
Market Place,
Knaresborough.
Tel.0423-866886

The earliest records of the market here date from 1206, although it is possible that a market has existed here since Alfred the Great. The first Charter appears to have been granted in 1310 when Edward 2nd. gave one to Peter de Galveston, Lord of Knaresborough. The town grew in importance because of its position at the centre of the dale between the uplands on one side, rich in cattle, sheep and lead-mines, and the corn growing lowlands on the other. It also has what is reputedly the oldest chemist's shop in England in the Market Place.

Now, it is a large bustling open market, very busy and obviously attracting people from all around the area. Everything, from a bike repair stall to hats can be found here and about all that was missing was any meat or bakery. However, there was plenty of everything else, good fabric stalls, lots of clothes stalls (25), household, china, leather goods, carpets and rugs, lamps and lampshades, D.I.Y. and pet foods. A wholefood stall was also going a good trade. Fruit and vegetables were there in abundance and it is a market well worth a visit (if you can find somewhere to park that is not too prohibitively expensive!) Unfortunately the 'Ordinary' as advertised on the illustration no longer seems to exist but it was a meal where all the local farmers would gather to exchange gossip.

Town. Knottingley.

County. Wakefield M.B.C. West Yorkshire.

Market Days. Friday.

Where. The market uses part of the large car-park at G.T. Smith's Superstore in Knottingley.

Early Closing.
Thursday.

Public Library,
Hill Top,
Knottingley.
Tel.0977-82407

This is quite a small market with not a great deal of choice. There were three stalls selling fruit and vegetables, sweets, toys, cards and lots of clothes!

Town. Leeds.

County. West Yorkshire.

Market Days. Tuesday and Friday are the traditional market days for the outside stalls but many of them are also there on Saturdays as well. On Thursday the outside market is a flea and secondhand one. The indoor market is open each day of the week.

Leeds Covered Market, c.1950. Reproduced by kind permission of Leeds City Council, Department of Municipal Services.

Where. The Market covers a large area off Vicar Lane in the centre of Leeds.

Early Closing.
Wednesday.

Central Library,
Municipal Buildings,
Calverley Street,
Leeds LS1 3AB.
Tel.0532-462017

Tourist Information Office,
19 Wellington Street,
Leeds LS1 4DG.
Tel.0532-462454

Two markets did exist in Leeds initially — both built around 1827. The larger one was the Central Market on the corner of Duncan Street and Call Lane, and the other, Briggate Market, was built between Briggate and Vicar Lane. The present Market Hall was re-built in 1902 and is now a listed building, although a disastrous fire in 1975 destroyed a large part of it. There is a rather fine Corn Exchange near to the market built in 1863.

The Market is a very large one and I think it would be true to say that virtually anything you want, you could buy there! The indoor market is vast and has separate meat, fish and poultry aisles as well as the other shop units. The choice here is immense, and helped by the nearness of other similiar retailers prices and quality are easily compared. Outside, there are many fruit and vegetable stalls as well as lots more and the whole area is very busy. A market not to be missed.

Plans are in hand for 're-development' (a phrase to bring dread to the heart of a confirmed market addict!) but I am assured that much of the area will stay the same and in fact part of the project includes the repair and refurbishment of the present market hall — the emphasis here being on a sensitive restoration and conservation of the building. Time will tell how successful the new market will be. Having seen some examples on my visits for this book, I cannot pretend to be very optimistic.

Town. Leyburn.

County. Richmond D.C. North Yorkshire.

Market Days. Friday.

Where. A large open market place in the centre of town.

Early Closing. Wednesday.   Cattle Market, Friday.

Public Library,
Thornborough Hall,
Leyburn.
Tel.0969-23127

Tourist Information Office,
Commercial Square,
Leyburn.
Tel.0969-23069

'There are few things more enjoyable in English life than a visit to Leyburn on a market morning'. So wrote the author in a book on Yorkshire published at the turn of the century and I think the same holds good today. It's a really nice country market with a good variety of things to choose. Lots of good fruit and vegetables, a really nice cheese van, complete with bow window (also seen at other markets in the area), two stalls selling good working clothes, a fish van doing a good trade and the usual selection of clothes and household goods. The market has been here since the late 17th century and it has been on a Friday since 1696. A market worth visiting that reflects very much the local community.

Town. Maltby.

County. Rotherham M.B.C. South Yorkshire.

Market Days. The open market is held on Tuesday, Friday and Saturday, whilst the Indoor Market opens on Wednesday as well.

Where. A modern indoor Market Hall is housed in the Arndale Centre, High Street, with the open stalls outside this building at the rear.

Leyburn Market, c.1920. Reproduced by kind permission of Dalesman Publishing Ltd.

Early Closing.
Thursday.

Public Library,
High Street,
Maltby.
Tel.0709-812150

A small market, this, serving the local community, but with quite a choice in the outside market particularly in stalls selling household goods. Most of the food was in the Market Hall.

Town. Malton.

County. Ryedale C.C. North Yorkshire.

Market Days. Saturday.

Where. This market is held in the most attractive market place in the centre of Malton.

Early Closing.
Thursday.

Public Library,
St. Michaels Street,
Malton.
Tel.0653-692714

Cattle Market, Tuesday,
Friday.

Tourist Information Office,
The Old Town Hall,
Market Place,
Malton YO17 0LT.
Tel.0653-600048

Malton did have a long history of a market here but it lapsed at some point (although the cattle market always thrived) and the street market was not revived until relatively recently. When I lived here in the early 1960's the 'market' was two or three rather miserable stalls tucked away round the side. Now it takes over the whole of the market place and is a great draw for the whole area. It's a lively and busy market, with lots of choice and variety. Put it on your visiting list!

Town. Market Weighton.

County. East Yorkshire D.C. Humberside.

Market Days. Friday.

Where. An open area off the main road with semi-permanent wooden stalls.

Early Closing.
Thursday.

Public Library,
Princess Road,
Market Weighton YO4 3BY
Tel.0696-73384

Two important charters were granted to Market Weighton in the Middle Ages. Firstly, Reginald FitzPeter was granted the market rights by Henry 3rd. in 1251 for a weekly market each Thursday, but subsequently Lord Vesci repealed this and obtained one for a market each Wednesday. At some point the day changed to a Friday and the day I was there (a rather cold and wet January day) it had only a small number of stalls, and by mid-afternoon they were all packing up.

Town. Masham.

County. Harrogate D.C. North Yorkshire.

Market Days. Wednesday.

Where. This open stall market is held in a very large open market square surrounded by interesting greystone buildings with the Church in one corner.

Early Closing. Thursday.   Cattle Market, Tuesday.

Public Library,
Bank Park Square,
Masham.
Tel.0765-89723

The first charter to hold a fair in Masham was given by Richard 2nd. in 1393 and later Geoffrey, Lord Scrope, obtained a Charter for a weekly market on a Wednesday.

In the Winter this market is quite small with only

about 20 stalls all selling what one market trader described to me as 'the basics'. However I am told that in the tourist season the market is much increased by stalls selling bric-a-brac and antiques. The 'off-season' market still has choices to offer, however, with clothes, food, cards, D.I.Y. etc.

Town. Mexborough.

County. Doncaster M.B.C. South Yorkshire.

Market Days. The open market is on Monday, Friday and Saturday, and the Indoor all week.

Where. There is a semi-permanent arrangement of open-air stalls in a square in a modern shopping precinct, with the Market Hall opening off this square.

Early Closing. Thursday.

Public Library,
Bank Street,
Mexborough.
Tel.0709-582037

A fairly small market serving this small town. On the Monday that I visited there were about 30 stalls with the usual range of products, but including a wine and beer making supply stall, football strip and accessories and window blinds.

Town. Middlesbrough.

County. Middlesbrough D.C. Cleveland.

Market Days. Monday, Thursday, Friday.

Where. The market here is at the rear of a modern shopping mall, the Hill Street Centre. There is also a covered Market Hall in the Centre.

Early Closing.
Wednesday.

Public Library,   Tourist Information Office,
Victoria Square,   125 Albert Road,
Middlesbrough,   Middlesbrough.
TS1 2AY   Tel.0642-245432 ext. 3580
Tel.0642-248155

A market has existed here since 1840 but this is obviously a new site. It is a small market selling mainly clothes although there are a few household stalls as well. The food mostly appears to be in the Market Hall.

Town. Morley.

County. Leeds M.D.C. West Yorkshire.

Market Days. Peel Street — Monday-Saturday,
                Queen Street — Tuesday-Saturday.

Where. There are two indoor Market Halls in Morley — Peel Street and Queen Street but there are no outside stalls.

Early Closing.
Tuesday

Public Library,
Commercial Street,
Morley.
Tel.0532-532780

The Queen Street market was built around 1880 and extended in the 1980's.
The two halls sell a very wide variety of anything and everything in small shop units. Lots of food, as well as clothes, fabrics, plants. etc.

Town. Normanton.

County. Wakefield M.B.C. West Yorkshire.

Market Days. Tuesday, Saturday.

Where. Open air in Westfield Street.

Early Closing.
Wednesday.

Public Library,
Castleford Road,
Normanton.
Tel.0924-893647

The market, of about thirty-five stalls, is in a pleasant modern shopping development and many of the open stalls are permanent with warm red tiled roofs. The area is surrounded by some small market shop units, mainly selling food, and some larger supermarkets. Lots of clothes stalls, some household, confectionery and bric-a-brac.

Town. Northallerton.

County. Hambleton D.C. North Yorkshire.

Market Days. Wednesday, Saturday.

Where. You cannot miss this large market as it spreads itself either side of the main road through the town!

Early Closing.
Thursday.

Cattle Market, Alternate
Tuesday and Wednesday.

Public Library,
1 Thirsk Road,
Northallerton DL6 1PT.
Tel.0609-6271

There is a Market Cross here which dates from 1777 but it is nearly obscured on market days by the stalls which surround it! This is a really good, interesting and varied market drawing people from a wide surrounding area. The Wednesday market is usually busier and bigger than the Saturday one. Lots of good fruit and vegetables, fish stalls (one with game as well!), the cheese van with its distinctive bow window, and all sorts of bakery and confectionery. The country nature of this market is emphasised by the two stalls selling men's warm working clothes and another stall selling horse tackle! Everything here with a wealth of choice — you can even buy leather tankards!

There is a W.I. Market on a Friday.

Town. North Ormesby.

County. Langbaugh D.C. Cleveland.

Market Days. Tuesday, Saturday.

Where. Market Place.

Public Library,
Derwent Street,
North Ormesby.
Tel.0642-247980

A local landowner and benefactor, Mr Pennyman, started this market in 1875, giving all the profits to the North Ormesby Hospital. He later handed over the rights to the local Urban District Council and in 1966, the local hospital was receiving an income of £4000. The hospital has now closed but the market is still thriving. Tuesday is the busier day with more stalls and it attracts people from the wide area around.

Town. Ossett.

County. Wakefield M.B.C. West Yorkshire.

Market Days. Tuesday and Friday (Craft and flea market in the Town Hall also on a Friday).

Where. The market is in an open square formed by a modern shopping development.

Early Closing.
Tuesday.

Public Library,
Station Road,
Ossett.
Tel.0924-270960

The market here is very modern, compared that is to many of the markets that have been established for hundreds of years. This one started in 1929 and moved to its present site around 1971. However, it seems that some stalls were erected around the site of the old Ossett Church in the latter half of the 19th century so the market may have had a longer history than records show.

There are about fifty stalls in the open market offering the usual array of goods. There were more food and grocery stalls than is often the case, but clothes of all types predominated.

The Craft and Flea market had some second-hand clothing stalls as well as jewellery and china, but it also had a good selection of hand-knitters showing off their wares.

Town. Otley.

County. Leeds M.B.C. West Yorkshire.

Market Days. Friday, Saturday.

Where. Open air street market in the Market Place and on Fridays all along Kirkgate as well.

Early Closing.
Wednesday.

Cattle Market, Monday at Leeds Road, East Chevin and Friday at the Bridge End Auction Mart.

Public Library,
4 Boroughgate,
Otley.
Tel.0943-463164

Tourist Information Centre,
Council Offices,
8 Boroughgate,
Otley.
Tel.0943-465151

The very first charter was granted in 1222 by Henry 3rd. for an annual 'feast' in the Churchyard, but then a further Charter allowed a weekly market to be held. This market, particularly on a Friday, is still a draw for all the locality and well worth a visit. The Buttercross (not a cross at all but a type of covered barn) was built to replace the ancient market cross, destroyed by lightning in 1871, and was used until 1939 to sell butter and other dairy products. Now somewhere to sit and watch the world but still used sometimes for charity stalls. The Jubilee clock next to the Buttercross was built to commemorate Queen Victoria's Jubilee in 1887 and has since had various memorial plaques added to it.

The market on Fridays is the bigger one with around 60 stalls, full of character and life. Unlike some of the other markets, it does not seem to deal exclusively in clothes but has a range of stalls with something for everyone. There is a good choice of fruit and vegetables, an interesting cheese van which sells local cheeses as well as Yorkshire curd, some good china stalls and an extensive haberdashery selection for keen dressmakers, who will also find stalls selling the material as well. Foam rubber and loose covers can also be found and a fish van does brisk trade. The day I went two buskers played and added to the atmosphere. Definitely a market not to be missed. The Saturday market has around 40 stalls, again with a range of goods but not quite such a wide selection to be found as on a Friday.

A W.I. market is held in Otley Civic Centre opening at 10.00 a.m. each Friday.

Town. Penistone.

County. Barnsley, M.B.C. West Yorkshire.

Market Days. Thursday, Saturday.

Where. Large open space at the rear of Market Street with the cattle market behind the retail market. The stalls are semi-permanent ones with rather a lot of corrugated iron around!

Early Closing.
Wednesday.

Cattle Market, Thursday,
Saturday.

Public Library,
High Street,
Penistone.
Tel.0226-762313

This is a busy market in what used to be a large sheep centre, but then changed its character quite radically when steel came to Sheffield and Penistone became an important staging post. There are now about 40 stalls with fish, fruit and vegetables, bakery and all the usual clothing and household stalls. Unusually, there was also a large trailer selling frozen food and a stall of winemaking materials.

Town. Pickering.

County. Ryedale D.C. North Yorkshire.

Market Days. Monday.

Where. The market takes over the wide main street, called the Market Place, in the centre of the town.

Early Closing.
Wednesday.

Public Library,
Bridge Street,
Pickering.
Tel.0751-72185

Tourist Information Office,
The Station,
Pickering YO18 7AJ.
Tel.0751-73791

It seems that the first Charter was granted by King John in 1201 and the market has flourished since then. Country and Western music and tapes, a toffee stall and one selling caps, ties and woollen socks make this market a little different, although all the usual stalls were well represented. It is not a very large market — only about twenty-five stalls, but is a friendly, local meeting place.

There is a W.I. Market on Thursday.

Town. Pocklington.

County. East Yorkshire D.C. Humberside.

Market Days. Tuesday.

Where. The market spreads down both sides of the very wide main street.

Early Closing.
Wednesday.

Public Library,
Station Square,
Pocklington.
Tel.075-92-3373

The market has only fairly recently been revived here, but the original Charter was granted in 1300 to Henry Percy to hold a weekly market on a Saturday, and this was still in being in 1673; but with bigger markets all fairly near to it, Pocklington struggled to survive. Now it is an interesting market with about forty stalls selling most things. Two fish stalls, a meat van and two fruit

Pocklington Market. Reproduced by kind permission of Yorkshire Evening Press.

and vegetable stalls were there but there were also about fourteen clothes stalls! Two plant and flower stalls, six household ones and a D.I.Y. as well as fabrics, pet foods and a card stall make this a pleasant market to potter around, if not a spectacular one.

Town. Pontefract.

County. Wakefield M.B.C. West Yorkshire.

Market Days. Saturday.

Where. Really the whole of the centre of the town! The stalls seem to spread everywhere and as most of the area is pedestrianised it makes it very pleasant to stroll around.

Early Closing.
Thursday.

Public Library,
Shoemarket,
Pontefract.
Tel.0977-795368

In the 13th century Edmund de Lacy obtained a Charter from the King for the burgesses of the town to hold a weekly market.

There are some interesting things to see here, notably the old Buttercross erected in 1734 in memory of Solomon Dupier by his widow Elizabeth, and the Town Pump dating from 1571 still stands at the Market Cross. The Market Hall is also an imposing stone building and the Town Hall, or Moote Hall, has one side colonnaded which was in use by market traders when I was there. Look out also for many of the street names in the centre — most date from the 13th century when the town expanded. Wool Market, Shoe Market, Roper Gate etc. are just some of them.

This is a very large market indeed and one not to be missed! Anything and everything is on sale here and with the Market Hall as well there can be little left out!

There is also a Craft and bric-a-brac market on Wednesdays.

Town. Pudsey.

County. Leeds M.D.C. West Yorkshire.

Market Days. Tuesday, Friday, Saturday.

Where. Open stalls on Weaver Green, an open space behind Church Lane and near to the Bus Station.

Early Closing.
Wednesday.

Public Library,
Church Lane,
Pudsey.
Tel.0532-564427

Tuesday seems to be a busier market day with more stalls and more choice. A fish van was doing good trade and there were more confectionery and cake stalls. Clothes stalls predominated, but there were also good fabric stalls and a comprehensive haberdashery one. Friday is also quite a busy market with food stalls of various types as well as china, household goods and fabrics and wool. The Saturday market has about 35 stalls with a preponderance of clothes and shoe stalls, but food stalls, of all types, seem very thin on the ground.

Town. Rawmarsh.

County. Rotherham M.B.C. South Yorkshire.

Market Days. Tuesday, Friday.

Where. Open air site near to the Gateway supermarket with semi-permanent stalls.

Public Library,
Parkgate,
Rawmarsh.
Tel.0709-522588

I made the mistake of arriving at about 12.00 p.m. on a Tuesday and most of the stall-holders had either already packed up or were in the process of so-doing!

I began to wonder if I was in France and not South Yorkshire! However, even when fully in operation this is only a small market.

Town. Redcar.

County. Langbaugh D.C. Cleveland.

Market Days. Sunday mornings until 2.00 p.m. (additionally a small street market has recently started up on Fridays in Saltburn Road).

Where. Redcar Racecourse.

Early Closing.
Wednesday.

Public Library,
Coatham Road,
Redcar.
Tel.0642-472162

Tourist Information Office,
Regent Cinema Building,
Newcommen Terrace,
Redcar.
Tel.0642-471921

Redcar did have a market as far back as 1366 but this lapsed and although it was eventually revived in 1922 the 'second birth' only lasted until 1951. The Sunday market started in 1972.

The Sunday market is a very big affair with around 150 stalls selling a great variety of things. People from a wide area make a point of visiting Redcar on a Sunday to go to the market.

Town. Richmond.

County. Richmond D.C. North Yorkshire.

Market Days. Saturday.

Where. The lovely old, and very big, cobbled Market Place in the centre of Richmond is the natural home for the market. The Market Place is thought to be one of the largest in England.

Early Closing.
Wednesday.

Cattle Market, Monthly,
Saturday.

Public Library,
Queens Road,
Richmond.
Tel.0748-3120

Tourist Information Office,
Friary Gardens,
Victoria Road,
Richmond DL10 4AJ
Tel.0748-3525

A market has existed here since the 12th century, but the Charter stipulating a Saturday market was not granted until 1268. The obelisk in the Market Place replaced an earlier Market Cross and was built in 1771. Originally there was a reservoir under the Cross which held 12,000 gallons of water to serve the town. Holy Trinity Church, in the middle of the Market Place, now houses the museum for the Green Howard Regiment, but it is one of few surviving churches to have had shops underneath it — the part now occupied by the Museum.

The market itself is rather small and quite a disappointment in such a near-perfect setting. The fruit and vegetable stalls were doing a good trade as were both the fish van and a cheese stall. Local Richmond fudge was

Market day in Richmond. Reproduced by kind permission of Hendon Publishing Co. Ltd.

on sale and there was an interesting local wood carving stall.

There is also a Market Hall, built in 1854, which was lively and busy whilst I was there. Again, some local crafts appeared to be on sale as well as local produce, and there was even a bicycle stall.

Town. Ripon.

County. Harrogate D.C. North Yorkshire.

Market Days. Thursday, Saturday.

Where. Large open market in the Market Square.

Early Closing.
Wednesday.

Public Library,
Skellgarths,
Ripon.
Tel.0765-2128

Tourist Information Office,
Wakemans House,
Market Place,
Ripon.
Tel.0765-4625

This market has been held for centuries on a Thursday and an early Charter was granted by Henry 1st. to the Archbishop of York in 1108 for an annual fair to be held here. The Wakeman's house, a Tudor building, can still be seen in the Market Place and the upstairs houses a small museum. The Wakeman seems to have been originally concerned with keeping order within the city. There is still a bell rung each Thursday at 11.00 o'clock to announce the start of the market, but the Obelisk in the Market Place is relatively modern having been erected by William Aislabie in 1781.

This is a large, busy market with a wealth of choice in most areas. Lots of clothes stalls, including a hat stall and a hand-knitted jumper stall. One of the clothing stalls specialised in what it called 'Mature Fayre' — plenty of nice warm Long-Johns, woollen vests and thick nightwear! Curtains, lace, wallpaper all could be found here as well as home-made cakes. As in many of the country town markets, stalls selling Wellingtons, thick trousers and work shirts were here and a choice of D.I.Y. stalls. Household goods, from duvets to kitchen equipment, were in good supply as well.

A market not to be missed.

A W.I. market is also held on Thurday morning in the Y.M.C.A., Water Skellgate.

Ripon Market, c.1905. Reproduced by kind permission of Hendon Publishing Co. Ltd.

Town. Rossington.

County. Doncaster M.B.C. South Yorkshire.

Market Days. Tuesday, Friday.

Where. Open air near to the centre of Rossington.

Early Closing.
Wednesday.

Public Library,
McConnell Crescent,
Rossington.
Tel.0302-868295

This is a small market of semi-permanent stalls, but on the Tuesday I was there many stalls were empty. Clothes stalls were much in evidence, but some food, a carpet stall, cards, fabrics etc. were also doing a reasonable trade.

Town. Rotherham.

County. South Yorkshire.

Market Days. Open market, Monday and Saturday. Covered Market Hall, Monday to Saturday.

Where. Large open space in a modern shopping development off Howard Street. The Market Hall opens into this square.

49

Early Closing.
Thursday.

Public Library,
Central Library,
Walker Place,
Rotherham.
Tel.0709-38212

Tourist Information Office,
Housed in the Public
Library.

A Charter was first granted to Eustace de Vescey in 1207 by King John, and later the ownership of the market was transferred to the Abbot of Rufford Abbey. The old market hall was destroyed so nothing now remains of the old buildings and this new development was completed in 1968.

This is a large and interesting open stall market with well over 150 stalls selling everything from brassware to leather jackets! Apart from lots of fruit and vegetable stalls most of the other food is to be found in the Market Hall, but a wide range of clothes and fabrics are outside with carpets, haberdashery, loose covers, cards, second-hand clothes and furniture all part of this busy market.

Town. Rothwell.

County. Leeds M.B.C. West Yorkshire.

Market Days. Saturday.

Where. Marsh Street Car Park.

Early Closing.
Thursday.

Public Library,
Marsh Street,
Rothwell.
Tel.0532-824280

Rothwell was granted a Charter to Edmund de Lacy back in 1250 by Henry 2nd, but the Market Cross only dates from 1864. The original one was apparently knocked down by accident and re-built.

This is a very small market with only a few stalls. The Saturday I was there, about 12 stalls were open.

Town. Scarborough.

County. North Yorkshire.

Market Days. Thursday (however, as this is a covered market, some stalls are open every day).

Where. Covered Market Hall off Westborough.

Early Closing.
Wednesday.

Public Library,
Vernon Road,
Scarborough.
Tel.0723-364285

Tourist Information Office,
St. Nicholas Cliff,
Scarborough YO11 2EP.
Tel.0723-373333

Scarborough has had a market since Henry 2nd. gave the rights to the burgesses in 1161, and the Museum still holds a large blue stone which was probably used for the ratification and agreement of bargains in the old Tollergate. Now, though, the market is entirely held in the Market Hall and appears to be trading for most days of the week although Thursday is still given as the official market day.

Town. Sedbergh.

County. South Lakeland D.C Cumbria.

Market Days. Wednesday.

Where. Open air and held in a large open space that is used as a car-park on other days of the week.

Early Closing.
Thursday.

Cattle Market, Friday,
Station Road.

Public Library,
Main Street,
Sedbergh.
Tel.05396-20186

Tourist Information Office,
72 Main Street,
Sedbergh.
Tel.05396-20125

The market grew up around the old cross roads where the roads from Kendal, Kirkby Stephen and Dent all met, but unfortunately an old market cross which used to exist was demolished in 1854 and, so legend says, became part of a farmer's gate post. However, there is still an old Market House, no longer used, but built with subscriptions from ex-pupils of Sedbergh School in 1858 and with a public Reading Room above it. This latter still exists in the same place, but is now the local Branch Library.

This is a small country market with between twenty to thirty stalls. The day I went it was pouring with rain, so some stall holders had not come Like many of the markets in the more tourist areas, there seem to be more stalls (and a greater variety) in the summer months.

A W.I. market is held on Fridays from 10.30-11.45 a.m. in the Masonic Hall.

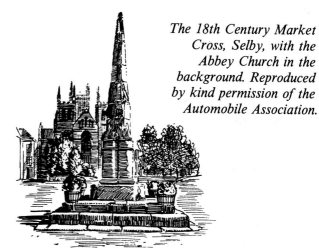

The 18th Century Market Cross, Selby, with the Abbey Church in the background. Reproduced by kind permission of the Automobile Association.

The Market Place, Selby. Reproduced by kind permission of Yorkshire Evening Press.

Town. Selby.

County. Selby D.C. North Yorkshire.

Market Days. Monday.

Where. An open market in both the Market Place and Wide Street, close to Selby Abbey.

Early Closing. Thursday.

Cattle Market, Friday.

Public Library,
Mickelgate,
Selby.
Tel.0757-702020

Tourist Information Office,
Bus Station,
Park Street,
Selby
Tel.0757-703263

The original market Charter, granted in 1304 to the Abbey of St. Germanus at Selby, stipulated that if the market was not held in the grounds of Selby Abbey, it should be as close as possible. This still holds good today and the market is held in the shadow of the abbey and right outside its door.

The old, rather weather-beaten market cross in admist all the stalls was originally erected in 1790.

This is a busy market with a good variety of stalls, although there was little food. Clothes and household goods seemed to predominate but there was also, unusually, a stall selling bicycle parts (perhaps reflecting the flatter terrain around here) as well as another for cosmetics. There were some fabric and wool stalls, china plus carpet and lino for sale, with about 50 stalls in all in a compact area.

Town. Settle.

County. Craven D.C. North Yorkshire.

Market Days. Tuesday.

The sign of the "Naked Man", overlooking the Market Square, Settle. Reproduced by kind permission of the Automobile Association.

Shambles (the old Butchers Row) and although these particular buildings are early 17th century below, the upper storey is Victorian. However, it is still quite easy to see the original plan of the lowered gulley with buildings above. There is also an obelisk in the square which would appear to be a war memorial as the original market cross was removed. Note also 'The Naked Man' cafe in the Market Place!

This is quite a large market with a cluster of stalls all around the Market Place. Everything from some nice local pottery to wholefoods. Two meat vans, fish, herbal remedies, fabrics, clothes, fruit and vegetables, tapes — all could be found here as well as lots more.

Where. The market is still held in the Market Place as it probably has been for centuries.

Early Closing.
Wednesday.

Public Library,
4 High Street,
Settle.
Tel.072-92-3456

Tourist Information Office,
Town Hall,
Settle BD24 9EJ.
Tel.072-92-3617

Henry 3rd. granted the first Charter for a market in 1249 and at one side of the Market Place there is still The

Town. Sheffield.

County. South Yorkshire.

Market Days. Both the Castle Market Hall and the Sheaf Indoor Market are open every day except Thursday. The Setts Open Market is open on Tuesday, Friday and Saturday. Monday is a Collectors Market, and Wednesday Secondhand.

Where. The Castle Market is a modern postwar building, put up in 1965 on the site of the old Sheffield Castle, as is the Sheaf Market on the opposite side of the road. This latter was opened in 1972. The Setts is an open area to the rear of the Sheaf Market with about 40 permanent stalls.

Early Closing.
Thursday.

Public Library,
Surrey Street,
Sheffield.
Tel.0742-734711

Tourist Information Office,
Town Hall Extension,
Union Street,
Sheffield S1 2HH
Tel.0742-734671

A Charter in 1296 granted to Thomas, Lord Furnival, confirmed a Tuesday as the market day then. The Castle Market is very large and bustling with lots of food to choose from and a wide variety of choice. The Sheaf is similiar although does not perhaps have quite as many food stalls. The day I went, the Setts Market was all secondhand clothing and was very busy. These three markets together are interesting in the range of goods they stock, but are all modern buildings with little in the way of atmosphere.

There is a W.I. Market each Saturday.

There is a further market, Moorfoot Market, on Tuesday, Wednesday, Friday and Saturday in the open precinct there.

Town. Shipley.

County. Bradford M.D.C. West Yorkshire.

Market Days. The Indoor Market Hall — Mondays to Saturdays.
Open air stalls — Friday, Saturday.

Where. The open stalls are in the Market Place with the Market Hall in a modern building on the other side of the road.

Early Closing.
Wednesday.

Public Library,
2 Wellcroft,
Shipley BD18 3QH.
Tel.0274-757150

The Friday market has around 25-30 stalls with fruit and vegetables and confectionery quite well represented. On Saturday there are about 25 open stalls with clothes and shoes predominating, but there are around five fruit and vegetable stalls with also two second-hand clothes stalls. If you are looking for clothes, then Saturday is probably the better day to go, but the market does not seem to have any special flavour to it.

The Indoor Market Hall is housed in a modern shopping block near to the market. This has 45 separate units in it and is open every day. There is a good delicatessen and a health food shop as well as all the other usual retail outlets.

An early view of Skipton High Street. Reproduced by kind permission of Hendon Publishing Co. Ltd.

Town. Skipton.

County. Craven D.C. North Yorkshire.

Market Days. Every day except Sunday and Tuesday.

Where. This market takes over both sides of the very wide main street and is impossible to miss!

Early Closing.
Tuesday.

Cattle Market, Monday and alternate Wednesday.

Public Library,
High Street,
Skipton.
Tel.0756-2926

Tourist Information Office,
8 Victoria Square,
Skipton.
Tel.0756-2809

Skipton started to grow when Romille, a Norman baron, built a castle there and that together with the influence of the nearby monks at Bolton Priory ensured that Skipton became an important cross-roads between Lancaster and York. The market assumed an even greater importance when the Leeds-Liverpool canal reached Skipton in 1774 and it seems to have never stopped growing since! The old Tolbooth is at one end of the Market Place and a plaque on it tells that underneath the actual Tolbooth were cells for felons. At each side of the steps are the remains of the town stocks.

Skipton is a very large, thriving market always busy and with lots to look at and buy. I visited it on a Wednesday and found about 60 stalls selling everything from whole-foods to frozen foods! Walking and camping equipment on sale reflected Skipton's place as a centre for these activities and there was also a Market Hall with stalls. A friend who was there on a Monday said it seemed even busier then so any day would seem to be a good day to see this market! Definitely one not to be missed!

There is a W.I. market on a Wednesday.

Town. South Elmsall.

County. Wakefield M.B.C. West Yorkshire.

Market Days. Tuesday, Friday, and Saturday.

Where. The market opens off the main Barnsley Road.

Early Closing.
Wednesday.

Public Library,
Barnsley Road,
South Elmsall.
Tel.0977-42578

A clock stands outside the market (stopped the day I was there), but it is a useful sign-post to the market.

I parked quite a way from the market and was not too sure which way to go. However, I just followed everyone else and arrived at this very busy and active market. Some of the stalls are semi-permanent and there are some shop units around the perimeter of the market area, mostly selling food, but the variety in the whole market is great. Everything from cameras, knitting patterns, home-made toffees and sweets to a section for secondhand and flea. This was one of the more unexpected 'good' markets and I enjoyed my visit to it.

Town. Sowerby Bridge.

County. Calderdale M.B.C. West Yorkshire.

Market Days. Tuesday, Friday, Saturday.

Where. The stalls here are semi-permanent and are by the river on Station Road in Sowerby Bridge.

Early Closing.
Wednesday

Public Library,
Hollins Mill Lane,
Sowerby Bridge.
Tel.0422-831627

Tourist Information Office,
40 Town Hall Street,
Sowerby Bridge.
Tel.0422-83526

There were many more food stalls here than is often the case including five fruit and vegetable and five confectionery and bakery stalls. Meat and fish were also available and there were quite a few stalls selling household goods. Some secondhand clothing was noticed as well as secondhand books. A pleasant little market of about seventy stalls with a good choice.

Town. Stocksbridge.

County. Sheffield M.B.C. South Yorkshire.

Market Days. Tuesday, Friday.

Where. Open air stalls off the main road in this predominately steel town.

Early Closing.
Wednesday,

Public Library,
Manchester Road,
Stocksbridge.
Tel.0742-882576

Not a very big market in an open space on to the main road. The day I visited, (a Tuesday) the market stalls were half empty and there were few people about. Clothes stalls seemed to predominate.

Town. Stokesley.

County. Hambleton D.C. North Yorkshire.

Market Days. Friday.

Where. Market Place.

Early Closing.
Wednesday.

Public Library,
Manor House,
Stokesley.
Tel.0642-711592

In 1223 John Fitz-Robert de Eure was granted a Charter by Henry 3rd. to hold a fair here and it would seem that the market is also very old. The Town Hall in the Market Place was built in 1853 to replace an earlier Town Hall and Tolbooth and behind this is a smaller cobbled square. In this can be seen the outline of the spot where the Market Cross, destroyed in 1783, used to stand. What is now public toilets, a shop and the Police Station were originally the Shambles, or Butchers Square Row.

This is not a very big market, but it is attractive and pleasant. There was a good variety on sale here including a wholefood stall, walking shoes and boots and fur hats as well as the more usual produce, food and clothes.

There is a fortnightly W.I. Market on a Friday.

Town. Tadcaster.

County. Selby D.C. North Yorkshire.

Market Days. Thursday.

Where. The market is held in the Central car park just off the main road through Tadcaster.

Early Closing.
Wednesday.

Public Library,
Station Road,
Tadcaster.
Tel.0937-835218

This is only a small market but when I went it was attracting quite a few lunch-time shoppers. There were about twenty different stalls, lots of clothes but also a good cheese stall, fish, carpets, animal foods and even a stall advertising new bathroom suites!

Town. Thirsk.

County. Hambleton D.C. North Yorkshire.

Market Days. Monday and Saturday, although Monday is the main market day.

Where. The market is all along and on both sides of the very wide main street.

| **Early Closing.** | Cattle Market, Thursday, |
| Wednesday. | Station Road, Thirsk. |

Public Library,	Tourist Information Office,
Finkle Street,	16 Kirkgate,
Thirsk.	Thirsk YO7 1PQ.
Tel.0845-22268	Tel.0845-22755

It would seem that the market has been held here since before 1145, when the Lord of the Manor was empowered to charge a toll on the stalls and by 1293 it was certainly held, as now, on a Monday.

The rather nice clock was erected in 1893 to commemorate the marriage of the Duke of York to Princess Mary of Teck.

The Monday market is the bigger one with around seventy stalls selling a wide variety of goods. A very large D.I.Y. stall, one selling spades and other implements plus a stall stocking Wellington boots, thick twill trousers and thornproof tweeds show that this is a market patronised by the local farming community. There are lots of other clothes stalls, food, including some local cheese, and a local nurseryman with plants and garden supplies. Towels, pictures, toffee, even double-glazing can all be found here.

Town. Thorne.

County. Doncaster M.B.C. South Yorkshire.

Market Days. Friday, Saturday.

Where. This is a small open market in the town centre.

Early Closing.
Thursday.

Public Library,
Fieldside,
Thorne.
Tel.0405-812862

A pleasant open area in the middle of the shopping area houses the market with about 30 stalls on the Saturday I was there. All the usual food and clothes but, unusually, one selling and servicing sewing machines.

There is a W.I. market each Friday.

Town. Thurnscoe.

County. Barnsley M.B.C. South Yorkshire.

Market Days. Monday. There is a bric-a-brac on Fridays.

Where. In the Market Place, Station Road.

Early Closing.
Wednesday.

Public Library,
Shepherd Lane,
Thurnscoe.
Tel.0709-890001

I visited this market on a Monday when there were about 35 stalls, many of them selling clothes. It is a fairly small market with little in the way of any specialities or great choice. Around one side there are some small shops two of which are butchers.

Town. Todmorden.

County. Calderdale M.B.C. West Yorkshire.

Market Days. The open market is on Wednesday, Friday, Saturday, with Thursday a flea and secondhand market. The indoor Market Hall is open each day.

Where. The open stalls (some of them semi-permanent) are in the Market Place on Burnley Road, and the indoor Market Hall is also here.

Early Closing.
Tuesday.

Public Library,
Strand,
Rochdale Road,
Todmorden OL14 7LB.
Tel.0706-815600

An interesting market that obviously attracts some slightly unusual stalls. As well as all the usual offerings there was a hat stall, a local artist selling local watercolours, and a stall devoted to scarves, stoles and shawls! Two very good fish stalls had a most comprehensive selection on display and all the fruit and vegetable stalls appeared to have polished their fruit! Clothes, household goods, china etc. could all be found and the indoor market also had lots of local specialities, including a tripe and elder stall. There were about fifty outdoor stalls and approximately forty indoor units.

Town. Wakefield.

County. West Yorkshire.

Market Days. Monday, Friday, Saturday (Monday is good for secondhand and antique stalls).

Where. A large open area in the centre of the town. There is also a modern covered market hall at one side selling food and a larger one at the opposite side with a great variety of small shop units.

Early Closing.
Wednesday.

Public Library, Drury Lane, Wakefield. Tel.0924-371231	Tourist Information Office, Town Hall, Wakefield. Tel.0924-370211

An old market cross was unfortunately demolished in 1866, much to many people's disapproval, so nothing is left of the old market buildings. This is a very big, busy market full of variety and choice. The Monday I went, there were at least 200 open stalls selling everything from hats to net curtains! I counted at least 15 fabric and wool stalls (and some good haberdashery ones as well), and there was a huge variety of clothing on sale at all prices and all qualities. West Indian fruits and vegetables were on sale as well as the more common sort and lots of 'speciality' stalls selling football kit, vacuum cleaner spares, Third World products, and lots more! The secondhand and flea stalls were ranged along one side of the market place and there were about 25 of those with clothes, books, bric-a-brac even secondhand baby equipment. The Food Hall housed the butchers and the fish stalls as well as one or two more food shops. A very good market well worth a visit.

Town. Wetherby.

County. Leeds M.D.C. West Yorkshire.

Market Days. Thursday.

Where. An open market held in the Market Place with the stalls arranged around three sides of the Town Hall.

Early Closing.
Wednesday.

Cattle Market, Monday.

Public Library,
Westgate,
Wetherby.
Tel.0937-63144

Tourist Information Office,
Council Offices,
24 Westgate,
Wetherby.
Tel.0937-62706

Henry 3rd. granted the first Charter in 1340 to the Knights Templar authorising them to hold a weekly market for the sale of agricultural produce. Over the centuries this has altered somewhat and now the market concentrates more on other goods, although good cheese and a wide selection of fruit and vegetables perhaps still reflect the flavour of the original market! This is not a very large market — about twenty-five stalls the day I was there, but there was also an Antique and Craft Fair in the Town Hall and the W.I. also hold a Thursday market.

In The Shambles, at the side of the Market Place, is a row of shops with a covered walk alongside which was built as a Market Hall to commemorate the coronation of George 5th. in June 1911.

Town. Whitby.

County. Scarborough D.C. North Yorkshire.

Market Days. Saturday.

Where. The Market Place.

Early Closing.
Wednesday.

Cattle Market, Monday,
Wednesday.

Public Library,
Windsor Terrace,
Whitby.
Tel.0947-602554

Tourist Information Office,
New Quay Road,
Whitby.
Tel.0947-602674

A market has been held here since Henry 6th. granted a Charter in 1445, and now the colonnaded Town Hall, built by Nathanial Chomley in 1788, together with the open space in front, serves as the focal point for the market. Country women used to bring in their produce and sit in the inside whilst in the room upstairs, the Courts Leet of the Manor were held. This is a very small market, now with only about five or six stalls. It seems a shame that it has sunk to only this when the surroundings seem so appropriate for a bustling street market.

Town. Withernsea.

County. Holderness D.C. Humberside.

Market Days. Sunday.

Where. Queen Street, Withernsea.

Early Closing.
Tuesday.

Public Library,
Queen Street,
Withernsea.
Tel.0964-612537

The market here is open from around 9.00 a.m. to about 5.00 p.m. but this may vary depending on the time of year. It is a large market, attracting a big crowd, with up to two hundred stalls selling a wide variety of goods.

Town. Wombwell.

County. Barnsley M.B.C. South Yorkshire.

Market Days. Friday, Saturday.

Where. There are two sites for the market, one near to the library and one on the other side of the road.

Early Closing.
Thursday.

Public Library,
Station Road,
Wombwell.
Tel.0226-753846

This is a small market with about fifty stalls selling the usual variety of products.

Town. Yeadon.

County. Leeds M.B.C. West Yorkshire.

Market Days. Monday, Friday.

Where. Open cobbled area in front of the Town Hall.

Early Closing.
Tuesday.

Public Library,
Town Hall Square,
Yeadon.
Tel.0532-503743

This is a small suburban market with only about 30 stalls and most of those selling clothes. One fruit and vegetable stall, a fish van and two confectionery stalls were the sole food sellers, but there were two household stalls and one selling pet food.

Town. York.

County. North Yorkshire.

Market Days. Every day except Monday.

Where. The Market is in a large open area in Newgate off The Shambles (this latter was the butchers' market in medieval York and still gives a vivid idea of what the

York Market, with the Minster in the background.
Reproduced by kind permission of Yorkshire Evening Press.

whole city must have looked like in the fifteenth and sixteenth centuries).

Early Closing.
Wednesday.

Cattle Market, Monday, Thursday.

Public Library,
Museum Street,
York.
Tel.0904-55631

Tourist Information Office,
De Grey Rooms,
Exhibition Square,
York YO1 2HB.
Tel.0904-21756

The market is busy here every day although some of the stalls (and therefore the character of the market) change each day. There are six permanent, and very good, fish stalls but all the rest are open stalls. The Tuesday market had about 80 separate open stalls and was good for fruit and vegetables, clothes (about 20 stalls), fabrics and some good china stalls. On the Wednesday I was there, more household stalls with a good choice of bed and table linen were in evidence and more books and bric-a-brac on sale. Some secondhand stalls were there on both days. It would seem there is no 'bad' day to visit the market here and, particularly with all the other attractions of this most splendid city, it is one to explore.

A local farmer in York St. Sampson's Square Market at the turn of the century.